play guitar wit

nü meta

imp bizkit, korn, rage against the machine, papa roach, linkin park and creed

CW00543941

Wise Publications
London/New York/Paris/Sydney/Copenhagen/Madrid/Tokyo

Music Sales Limited
8/9 Frith Street,
London W1D 3JB, England.
Music Sales Pty Limited
120 Rothschild Avenue,
Rosebery, NSW 2018, Australia.

Order No. AM970519
ISBN 0-7119-8872-2
This book © Copyright 2001
by Wise Publications

Music arranged by Martin Shellard
Music processed by Andrew Shiels
Cover photographs courtesy of LFI and Retna
Printed in the United Kingdom by
Caligraving Limited, Thetford, Norfolk.

CD recorded by Martin Shellard
All guitars by Martin Shellard

Your Guarantee of Quality

As publishers, we strive to produce
every book to the highest commercial standards.
The music has been freshly engraved and the book has
been carefully designed to minimise awkward page turns
and to make playing from it a real pleasure.
Particular care has been given to specifying acid-free,
neutral-sized paper made from pulps which have not been
elemental chlorine bleached. This pulp is from farmed
sustainable forests and was produced with
special regard for the environment.
Throughout, the printing and binding have been planned
to ensure a sturdy, attractive publication which
should give years of enjoyment.
If your copy fails to meet our high standards,
please inform us and we will gladly replace it.

Music Sales' complete catalogue describes thousands of titles
and is available in full colour sections by subject, direct from
Music Sales Limited. Please state your areas of interest
and send a cheque/postal order for £1.50 for postage to:
Music Sales Limited, Newmarket Road,
Bury St. Edmunds, Suffolk IP33 3YB.

www.musicsales.com

guitar tablature explained

Guitar music can be notated three different ways: on a musical stave, in tablature, and in rhythm slashes

RHYTHM SLASHES are written above the stave. Strum chords in the rhythm indicated. Round noteheads indicate single notes.

THE MUSICAL STAVE shows pitches and rhythms and is divided by lines into bars. Pitches are named after the first seven letters of the alphabet.

TABLATURE graphically represents the guitar fingerboard. Each horizontal line represents a string, and each number represents a fret.

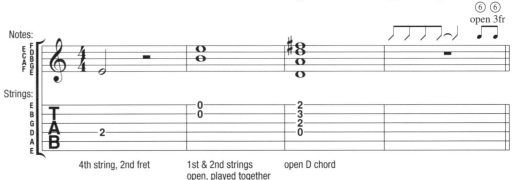

4th string, 2nd fret | 1st & 2nd strings open, played together | open D chord

definitions for special guitar notation

SEMI-TONE BEND: Strike the note and bend up a semi-tone (1/2 step).

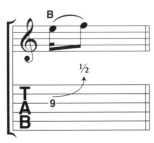

WHOLE-TONE BEND: Strike the note and bend up a whole-tone (whole step).

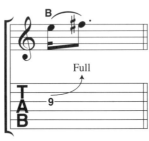

GRACE NOTE BEND: Strike the note and bend as indicated. Play the first note as quickly as possible.

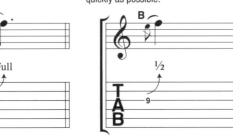

QUARTER-TONE BEND: Strike the note and bend up a 1/4 step.

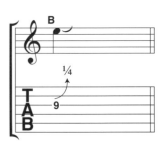

BEND & RELEASE: Strike the note and bend up as indicated, then release back to the original note.

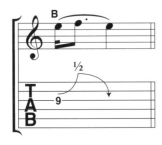

COMPOUND BEND & RELEASE: Strike the note and bend up and down in the rhythm indicated.

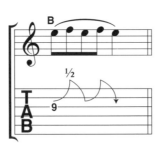

PRE-BEND: Bend the note as indicated, then strike it.

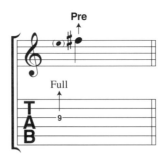

PRE-BEND & RELEASE: Bend the note as indicated. Strike it and release the note back to the original pitch.

UNISON BEND: Strike the two notes simultaneously and bend the lower note up to the pitch of the higher.

BEND & RESTRIKE: Strike the note and bend as indicated then restrike the string where the symbol occurs.

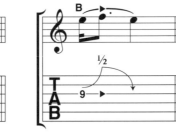

BEND, HOLD AND RELEASE: Same as bend and release but hold the bend for the duration of the tie.

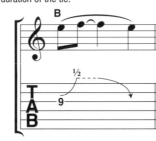

BEND AND TAP: Bend the note as indicated and tap the higher fret while still holding the bend.

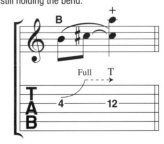

VIBRATO: The string is vibrated by rapidly bending and releasing the note with the fretting hand.

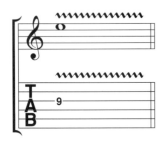

HAMMER-ON: Strike the first (lower) note with one finger, then sound the higher note (on the same string) with another finger by fretting it without picking.

PULL-OFF: Place both fingers on the notes to be sounded, Strike the first note and without picking, pull the finger off to sound the second (lower) note.

LEGATO SLIDE (GLISS): Strike the first note and then slide the same fret-hand finger up or down to the second note. The second note is not struck.

NOTE: The speed of any bend is indicated by the music notation and tempo.

SHIFT SLIDE (GLISS & RESTRIKE): Same as legato slide, except the second note is struck.

TRILL: Very rapidly alternate between the notes indicated by continuously hammering on and pulling off.

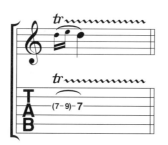

TAPPING: Hammer ("tap") the fret indicated with the pick-hand index or middle finger and pull off to the note fretted by the fret hand.

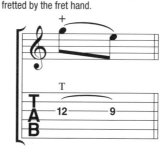

PICK SCRAPE: The edge of the pick is rubbed down (or up) the string, producing a scratchy sound.

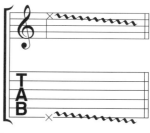

MUFFLED STRINGS: A percussive sound is produced by laying the fret hand across the string(s) without depressing, and striking them with the pick hand.

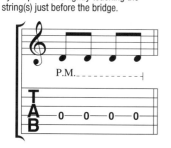

NATURAL HARMONIC: Strike the note while the fret-hand lightly touches the string directly over the fret indicated.

PINCH HARMONIC: The note is fretted normally and a harmonic is produced by adding the edge of the thumb or the tip of the index finger of the pick hand to the normal pick attack.

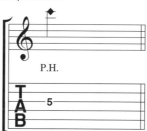

HARP HARMONIC: The note is fretted normally and a harmonic is produced by gently resting the pick hand's index finger directly above the indicated fret (in parentheses) while the pick hand's thumb or pick assists by plucking the appropriate string.

PALM MUTING: The note is partially muted by the pick hand lightly touching the string(s) just before the bridge.

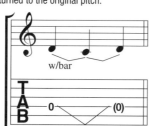

RAKE: Drag the pick across the strings indicated with a single motion.

TREMOLO PICKING: The note is picked as rapidly and continuously as possible.

ARPEGGIATE: Play the notes of the chord indicated by quickly rolling them from bottom to top.

SWEEP PICKING: Rhythmic downstroke and/or upstroke motion across the strings.

VIBRATO DIVE BAR AND RETURN: The pitch of the note or chord is dropped a specific number of steps (in rhythm) then returned to the original pitch.

VIBRATO BAR SCOOP: Depress the bar just before striking the note, then quickly release the bar.

VIBRATO BAR DIP: Strike the note and then immediately drop a specific number of steps, then release back to the original pitch.

additional musical definitions

> (accent)	• Accentuate note (play it louder).	
∧ (accent)	• Accentuate note with great intensity.	
• (staccato)	• Shorten time value of note.	
⊓	• Downstroke	
V	• Upstroke	

D.%. al Coda

D.C. al Fine

tacet

- Go back to the sign (%), then play until the bar marked *To Coda* ⊕ then skip to the section marked ⊕ *Coda*.

- Go back to the beginning of the song and play until the bar marked *Fine* (end).

- Instrument is silent (drops out).

- Repeat bars between signs.

- When a repeated section has different endings, play the first ending only the first time and the second ending only the second time.

NOTE: Tablature numbers in parentheses mean: 1. The note is sustained, but a new articulation (such as hammer on or slide) begins.
2. A note may be fretted but not necessarily played.

5

falling away from me

Words & Music by Korn

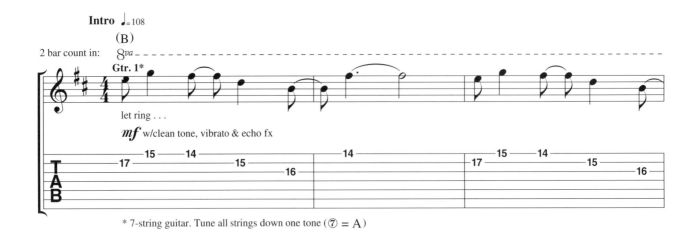

* 7-string guitar. Tune all strings down one tone (⑦ = A)

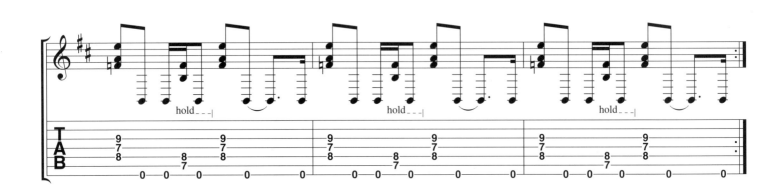

7

Fall-ing a-way from me. It's spin-ning round and

round. Fall-ing a-way from me. It's lost and can't be found. Fall-ing a-way from

D. 𝄋 al Coda ⊕

me. It's spin-ning round and round. Fall-ing a-way from___ me___ slow it down!

It's fall-ing a-way___ from me.___ Life's fall-ing a-way___

_from me.___ Fall!

Fmaj7/B

Gtr. 2

ff w/distortion   hold___|

hold___| hold___| hold___|

Chorus   B5   F#5   D5   C5   B5   F#5

ground. Beat-ing me down
Scream-ing so sound   beat-ing me beat-ing me down,

11

last resort

Words & Music by Papa Roach

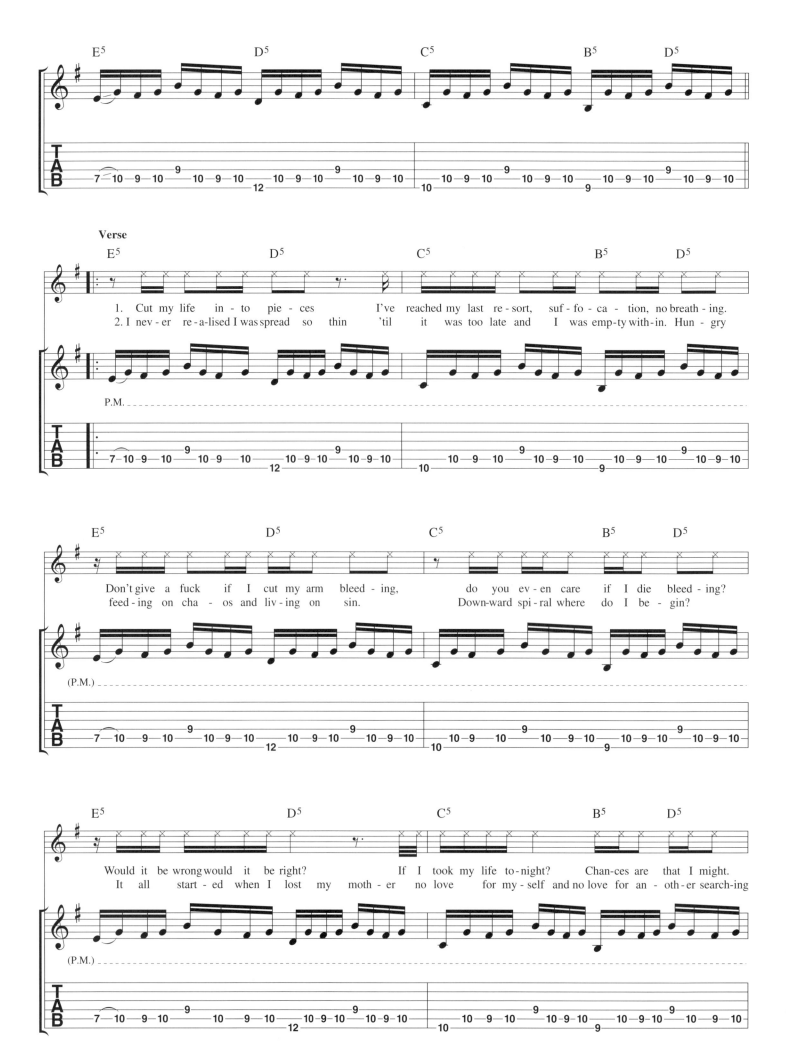

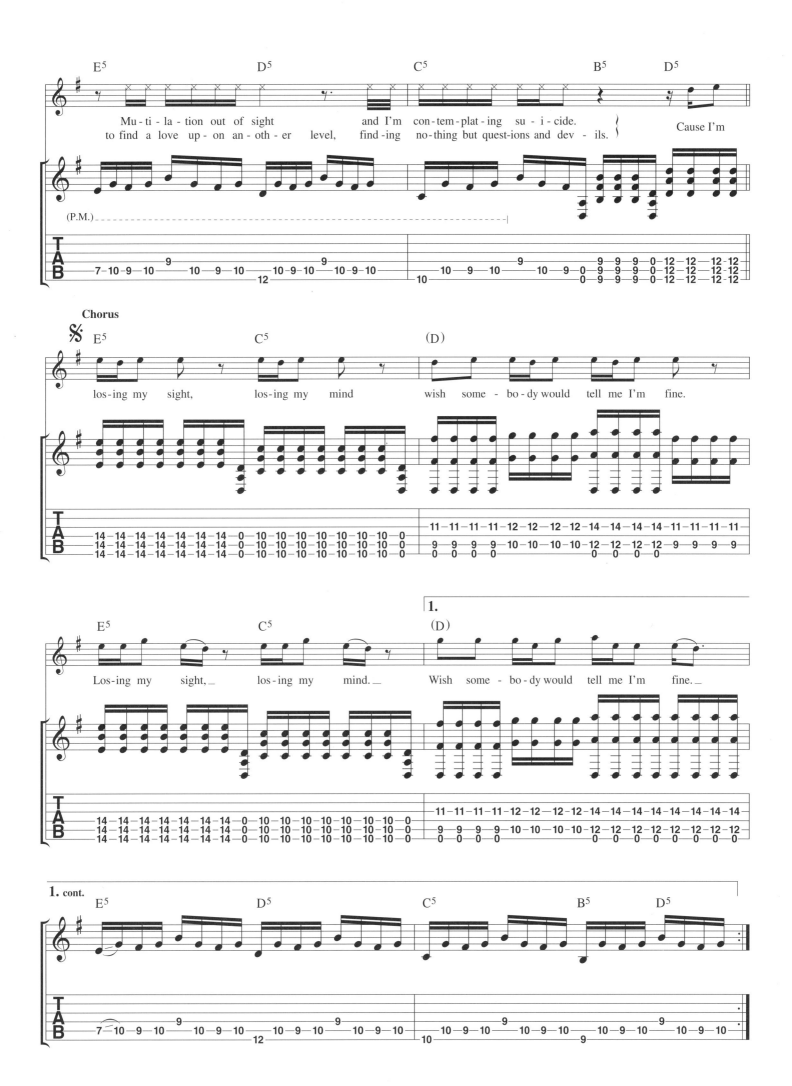

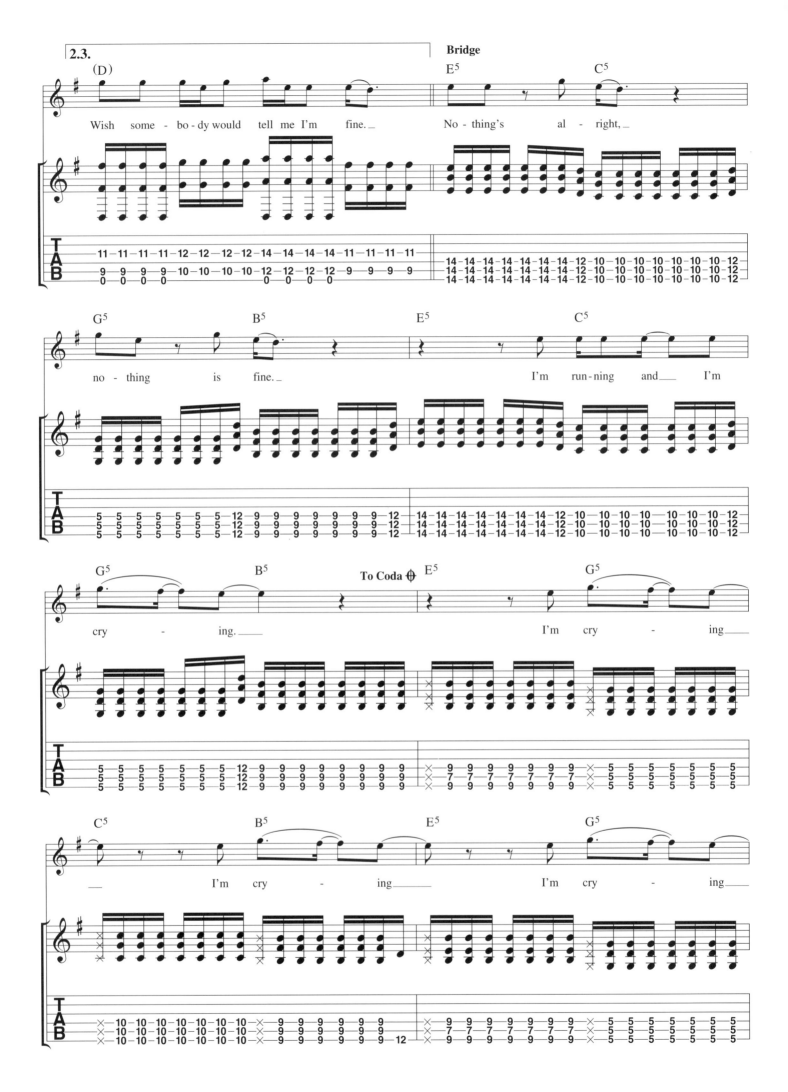

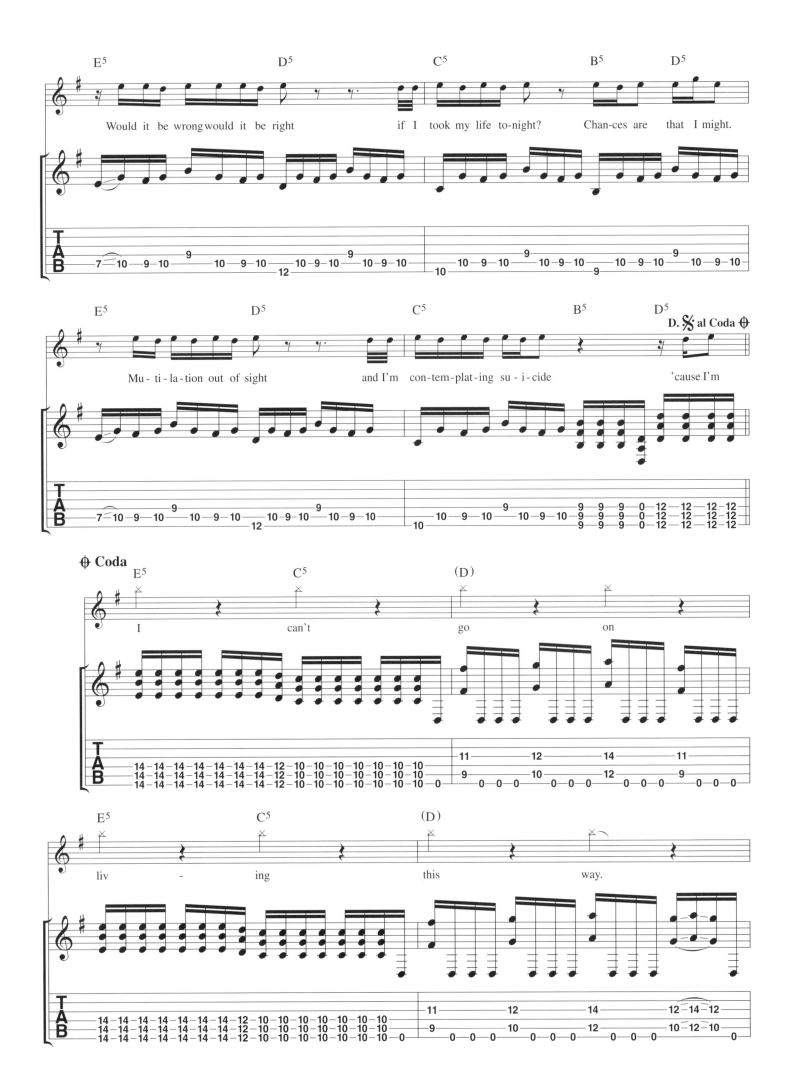

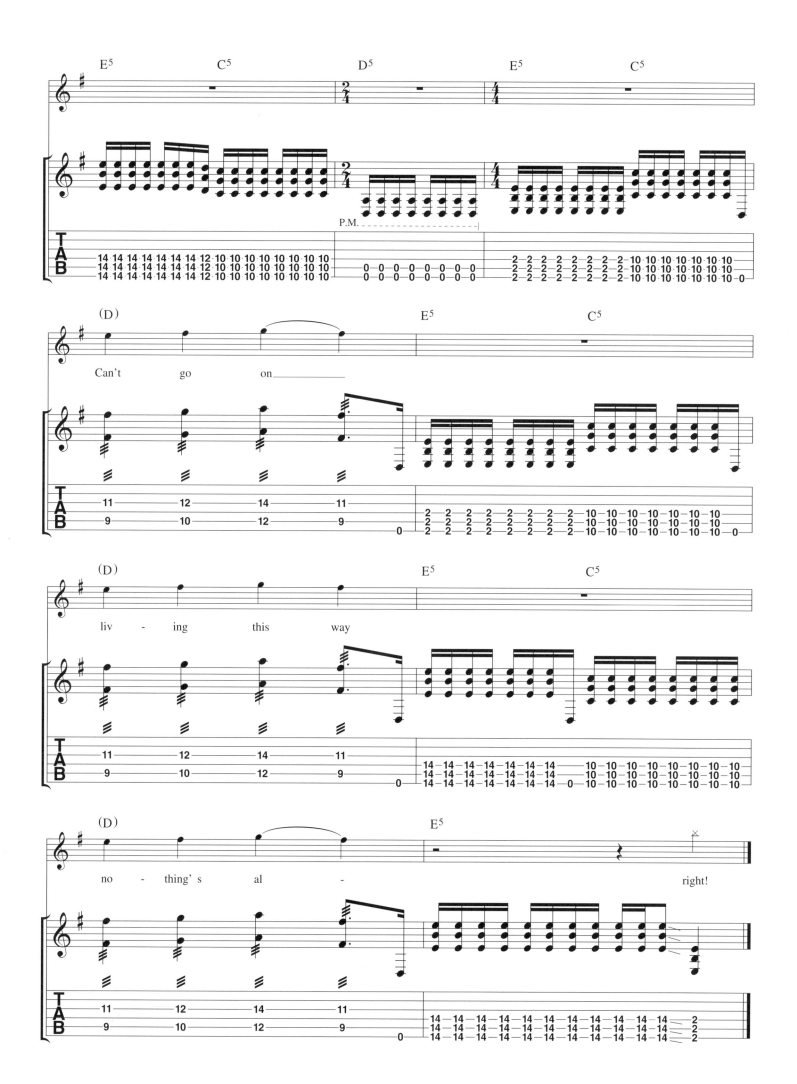

take a look around

Music by Lalo Schifrin
Words by Fred Durst

beat - ing up my mind ev - 'ry se - cond with my fist.

And ev - 'ry - bo - dy wan - na run, ev - 'ry - bo - dy wan - na hide from the gun.

You can take a ride through this life if you want but you can't take the edge off the knife no sir!

And now you want your mon - ey back, but you're de - nied but your brain's fried from the sack.

play guitar with...
all these

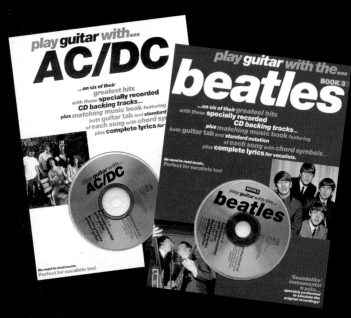

AC/DC
includes:
back in black
highway to hell
whole lotta rosie
Order No. AM955900

the beatles
includes:
day tripper
get back
yesterday
Order No. NO90665

the beatles book 2
includes:
eight days a week
please please me
ticket to ride
Order No. NO90667

the beatles book 3
includes:
here comes the sun
revolution
while my guitar gently weeps
Order No. NO90689

chuck berry
includes:
around and around
johnny b. goode
no particular place to go
Order No. AM943789

black sabbath
includes:
iron man
paranoid
war pigs
Order No. AM955911

blur
includes:
country house
girls and boys
parklife
Order No. AM935320

bon jovi
includes:
livin' on a prayer
wanted dead or alive
you give love a bad name
Order No. AM92558

eric clapton
includes:
layla
sunshine of your love
tears in heaven
Order No. AM950862

phil collins
includes:
another day in paradise
don't lose my number
one more night
Order No. AM928147

the corrs
includes:
forgiven, not forgotten
so young
what can i do
Order No. AM960971

the cranberries
includes:
hollywood
ridiculous thoughts
zombie
Order No. AM941699

dire straits
includes:
money for nothing
romeo and juliet
sultans of swing
Order No. DG70735

david gilmour
includes:
learning to fly
on the turning away
take it back
Order No.AM954602

buddy holly
includes:
rave on
words of love
peggy sue
Order No. AM943734

john lee hooker
includes:
boom boom
the healer
i'm in the mood
Order No. AM951885

b.b. king
includes:
every day I have the blues
rock me baby
the thrill is gone
Order No. AM951874

the kinks
includes:
all day and all of the night
waterloo sunset
you really got me
Order No. AM951863

kula shaker
includes:
govinda
hey dude
hush
Order No. AM943767

john lennon
includes:
cold turkey
happy xmas (war is over)
woman
Order No. AM943756

top bands and artists

bob marley
includes:
i shot the sheriff
jamming
no woman, no cry
Order No. AM937739

metallica
includes:
enter sandman
fade to black
the unforgiven
Order No. AM92559

metallica book 2
includes:
creeping death
seek and destroy
whiskey in the jar
Order No. AM955977

alanis morissette
includes:
hand in my pocket
ironic
you oughta know
Order No. AM943723

oasis
includes:
cigarettes & alcohol
morning glory
supersonic
Order No. AM935330

ocean colour scene
includes:
the circle
the day we caught the train
the riverboat song
Order No. AM943712

elvis presley
includes:
all shook up
blue suede shoes
hound dog
Order No. AM937090

pulp
includes:
common people
disco 2000
sorted for e's & wizz
Order No. AM938124

the rolling stones
includes:
brown sugar
(i can't get no) satisfaction
jumpin' jack flash
Order No. AM90247

sting
includes:
an englishman in
new york
fields of gold
if you love somebody
set them free
Order No. AM928092

the stone roses
includes:
i am the resurrection
i wanna be adored
ten storey love song
Order No. AM943701

the stone roses book 2
includes:
fool's gold
love spreads
one love
Order No. AM955890

suede
includes:
animal nitrate
electricity
we are the pigs
Order No. AM955955

paul weller
includes:
the changingman
out of the sinking
wild wood
Order No. AM937827

the who
includes:
i can see for miles
pinball wizard
substitute
Order No. AM955867

the 60's
includes:
all along the watchtower
(jimi hendrix)
born to be wild
(steppenwolf)
not fade away
(the rolling stones)
Order No. AM957748

the 70's
includes:
all right now (free)
hotel california
(the eagles)
live and let die (wings)
Order No. AM957759

the 80's
includes:
addicted to love
(robert palmer)
need you tonight (inxs)
where the streets have
no name (U2)
Order No. AM957760

the 90's
includes:
everything must go
(manic street preachers)
love is the law (the seahorses)
wonderwall (oasis)
Order No. AM957770

play guitar with...

sample the whole series with these special compilations...

the gold book

includes eight classic tracks:
jailhouse rock (elvis presley)
johnny b. goode (chuck berry)
layla (eric clapton)
sultans of swing (dire straits)
the healer (john lee hooker)
ticket to ride (the beatles)
woman (john lennon)
you really got me (the kinks)
Order No. AM951907

the platinum book

includes seven great songs:
*a design for life
  (manic street preachers)*
cigarettes & alcohol (oasis)
disco 2000 (pulp)
elephant stone (stone roses)
govinda (kula shaker)
the changingman (paul weller)
*the riverboat song
  (ocean colour scene)*
Order No. AM951918

Arthur Dick *has transcribed the music and provided the recorded guitar parts for most of the titles in the play guitar with... series, often bringing in other professional specialist musicians to achieve the most authentic sounds possible!*

A session guitarist with over twenty years' experience, he has worked with Cliff Richard, Barbara Dickson, Helen Shapiro, Bernie Flint and Chris Rea among others.

Arthur has played in many West End stage shows, and is in regular demand as a session player for TV, radio, and advertising productions.

He currently lectures on jazz and contemporary guitar at University Goldsmith's College, and works as a freelance production consultant.

Available from all good music retailers or, in case of difficulty, contact:

Music Sales Limited
Newmarket Road,
Bury St. Edmunds,
Suffolk IP33 3YB.
telephone 01284 725725
fax 01284 702592

www.musicsales.com

PUB04634

Now I know why you wan-na hate me 'cause hate is all the world has ev-en seen late-ly.

'Cause hate is all the world has ev-en seen late-ly.

'Cause hate is all the world has ev-en seen late-ly.

Outro
(F♯)

Repeat to fade

Gtr. 1 *8va*

one step closer

Words & Music by Chester Bennington, Rob Bourdon, Brad Delson, Joseph Hahn & Mike Shinoda

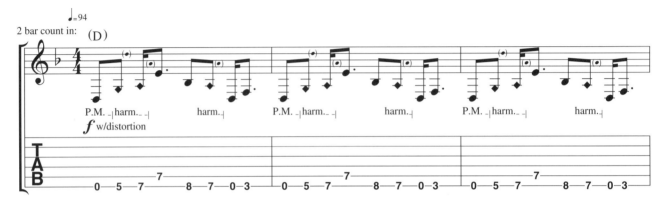

Tune all strings down a semitone.
Tune ⑥ = C♯

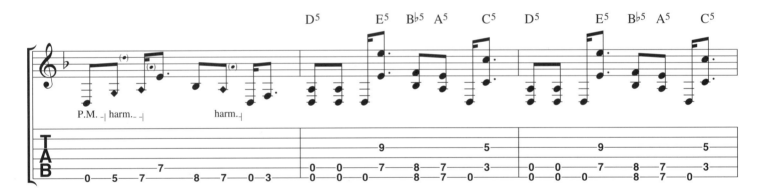

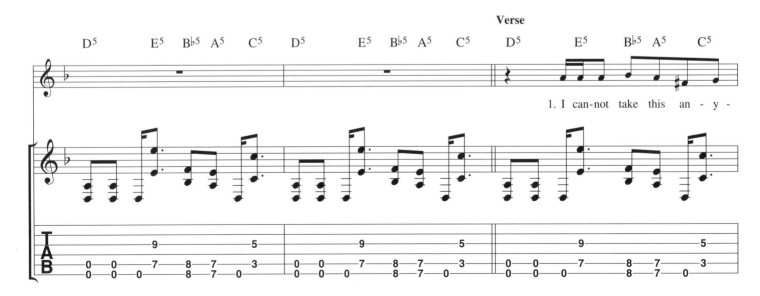

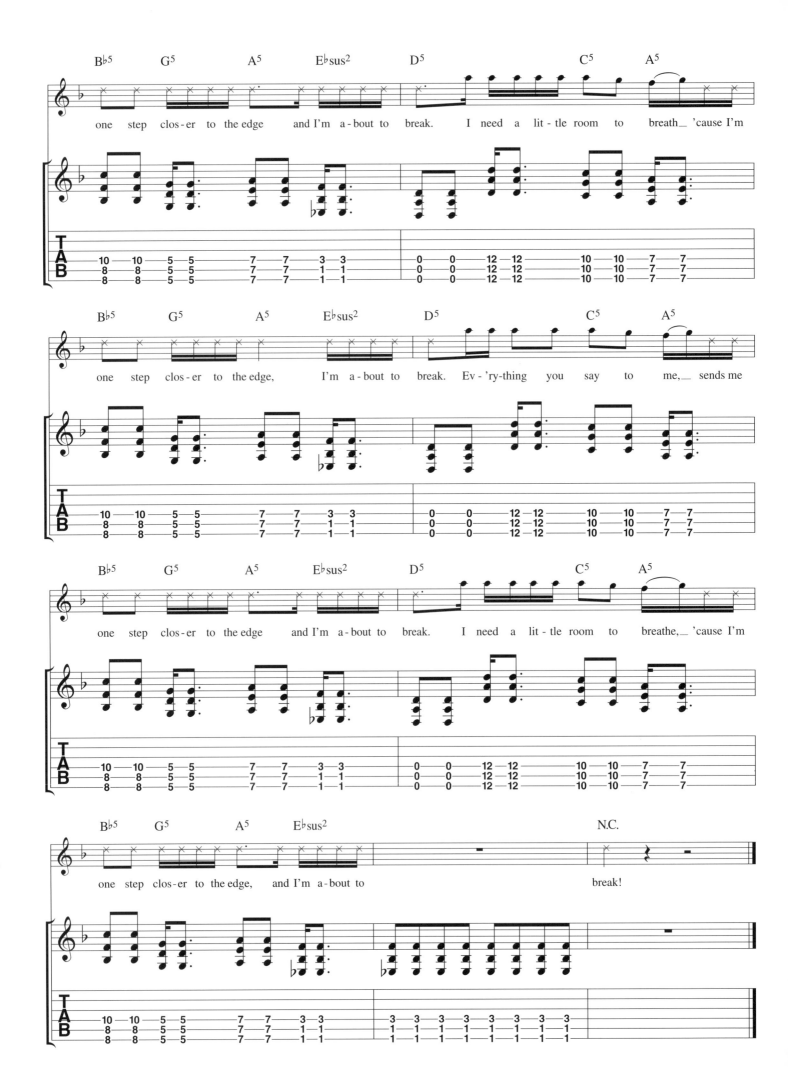

what if

Words & Music by Mark Tremonti & Scott Stapp

Intro ♩=52

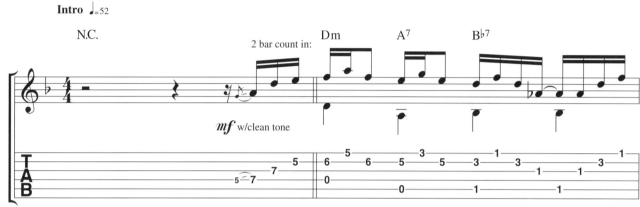

Tune ⑥ = D

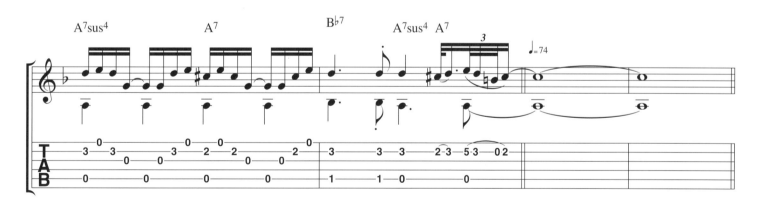

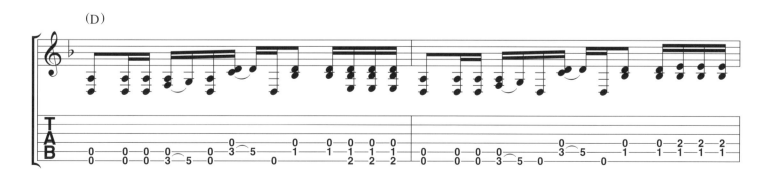

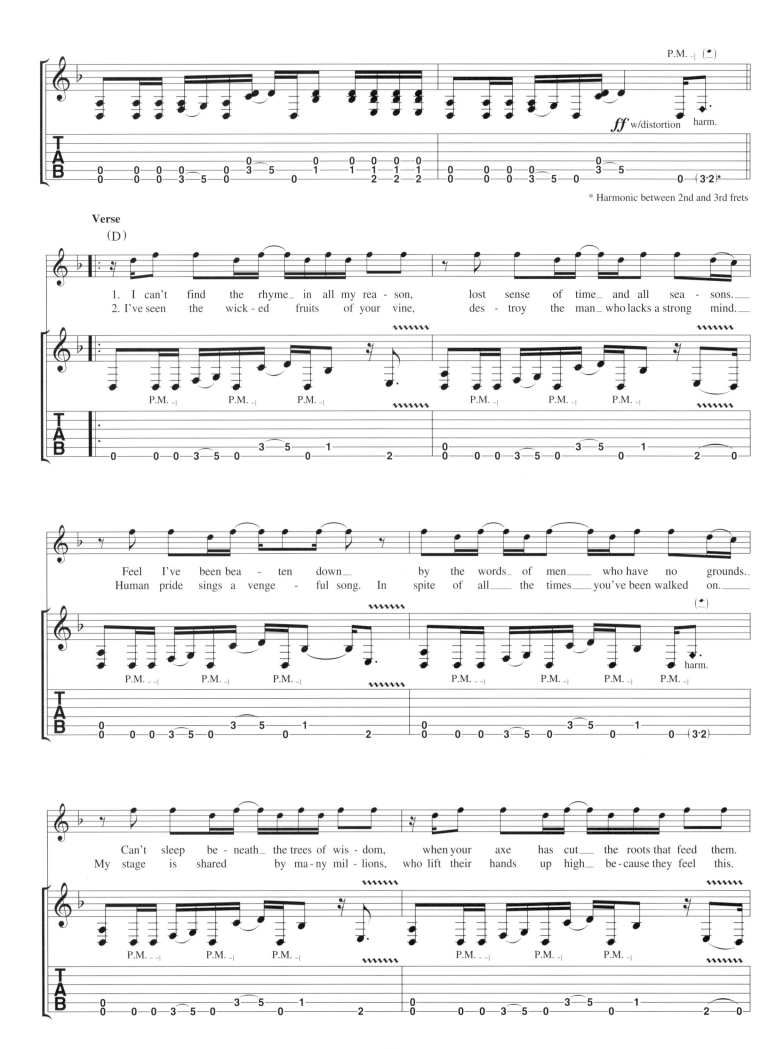

* Harmonic between 2nd and 3rd frets

Verse

(D)

1. I can't find the rhyme_ in all my rea - son,   lost sense of time_ and all sea - sons.
2. I've seen the wick - ed fruits of your vine,   des - troy the man_ who lacks a strong mind.

Feel I've been bea - ten down_   by the words_ of men_ who have no grounds.
Human pride sings a venge - ful song. In   spite of all_ the times_ you've been walked on._

Can't sleep be - neath_ the trees of wis - dom,   when your axe has cut_ the roots that feed them.
My stage is shared by ma - ny mil - lions, who lift their hands up high_ be - cause they feel this.

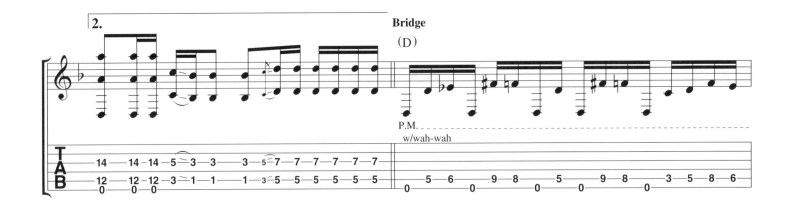

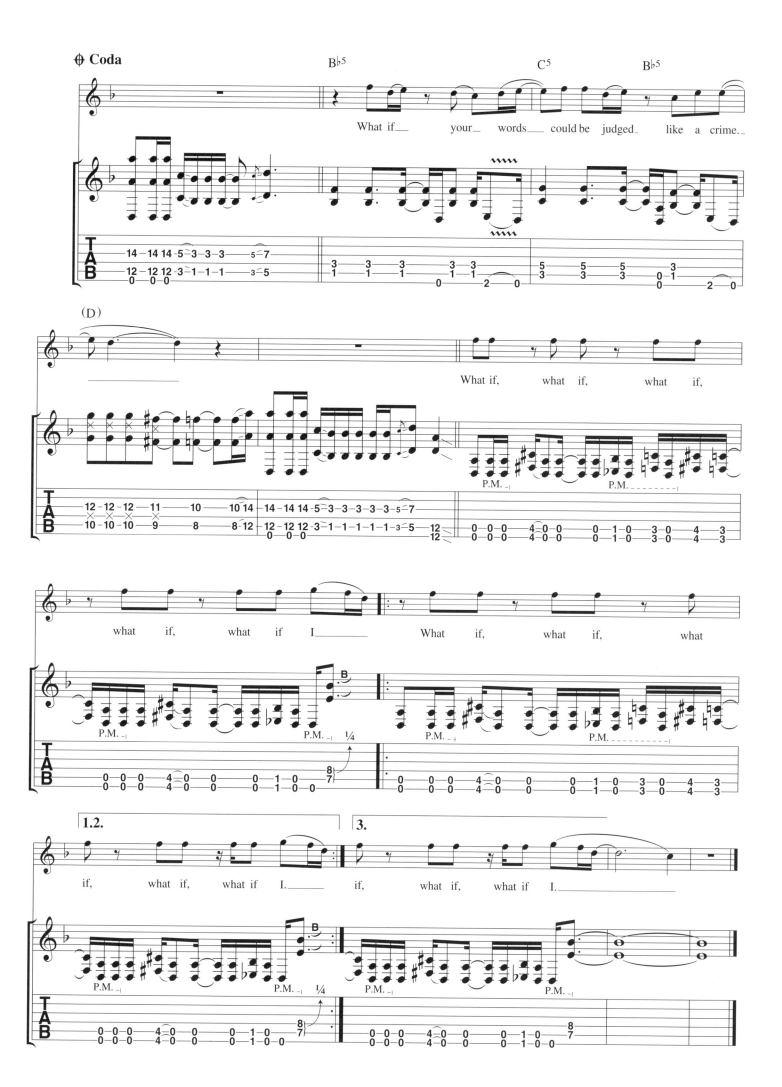

wake up

Words by Zack De La Rocha
Music by Rage Against The Machine

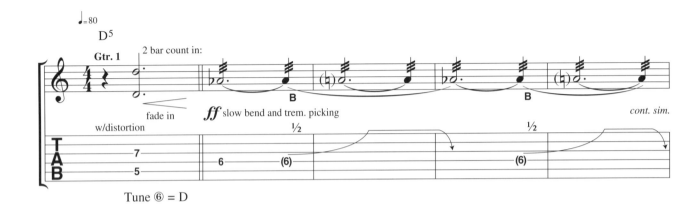

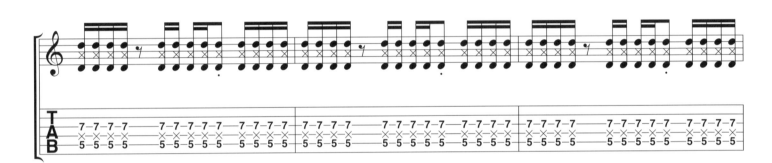

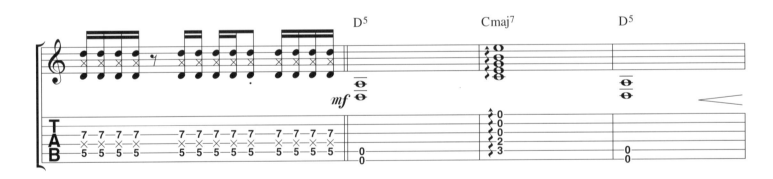

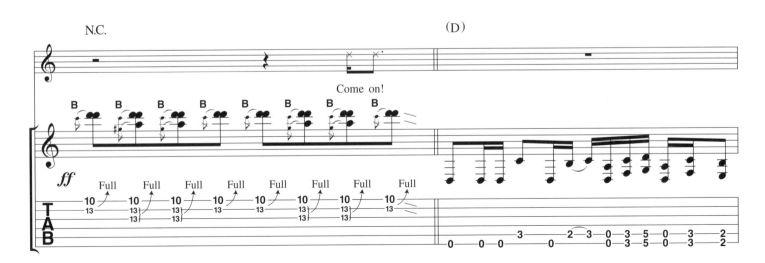

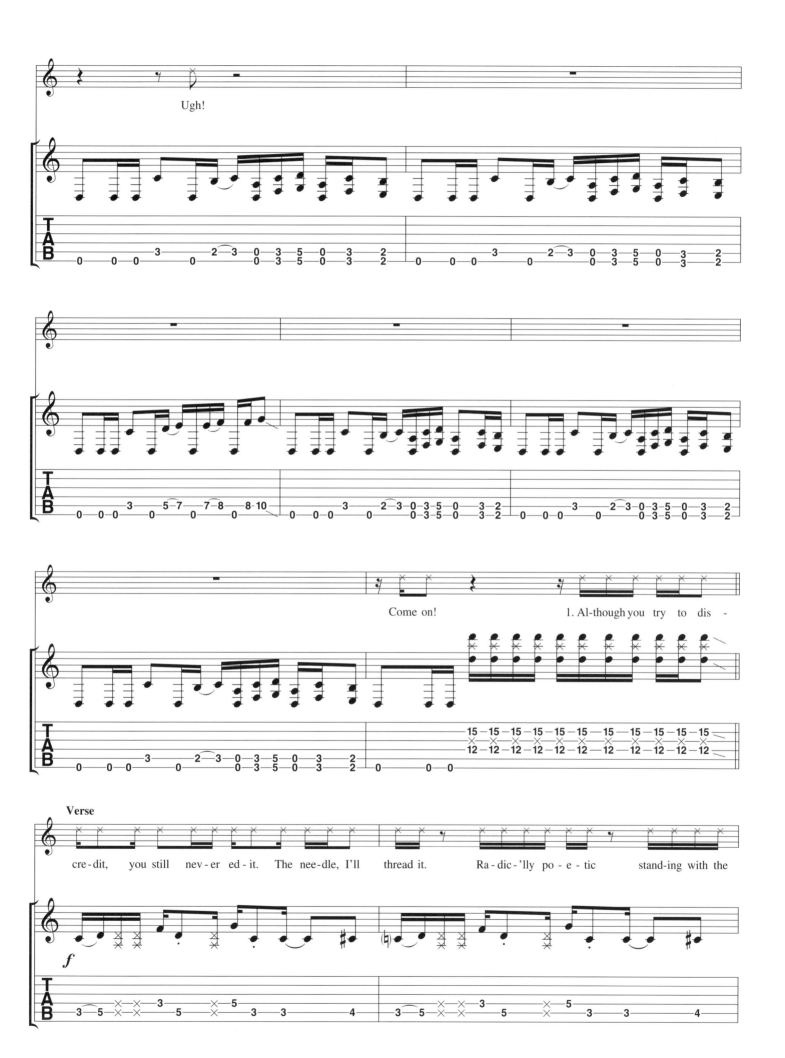

fu - ry that they had in six - ty six and like E - dou-ble I'm mad__ still knee-deep in the sys - tem's shit.

Hoo-ver, he was a bo-dy re-mov-er, I'll give you a dose,__ but it will nev-er come close__ to the rage

built up in - side of me, fist in the air in the land of hy - po - cri - sy.

2. Move - ments come and move - ments go, lead-ers speak, move-ments cease when their heads are down.__

blood still flows in the gut-ter. I'm like tak-in' pho-tos, mad boy kicks o-pen the shut-ter,

set the groove then stick and move like I was Cas-si-us rip the stut-ter step then bomb a left up-on the fasc-ists.

Yeah the se-ve-ral Fe-der-al men who pulled schemes on the dream and put it to an end. Ya

bet-ter be-ware of re-tri-bu-tion with mind_ war, twen-ty, twen-ty vi-sion and mu-rals with me-ta-phors.

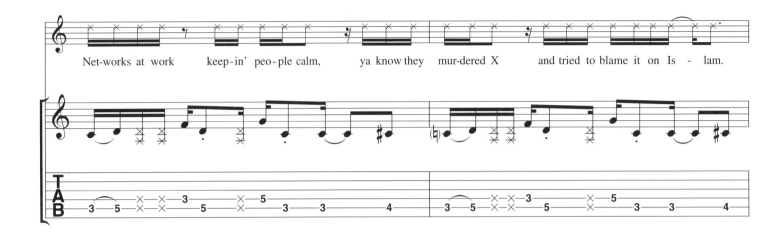

Net-works at work keep-in' peo-ple calm, ya know they mur-dered X and tried to blame it on Is - lam.

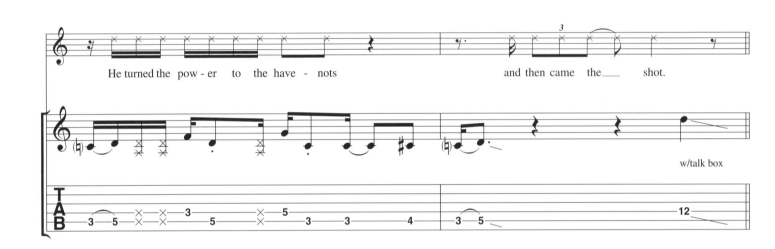

He turned the pow - er to the have - nots and then came the___ shot.

w/talk box

Solo

D⁵　　　　　　　　　　C⁵　　　　　　　　　F⁵

Gtr. 2

hammer-on w/left hand
w/selector switch

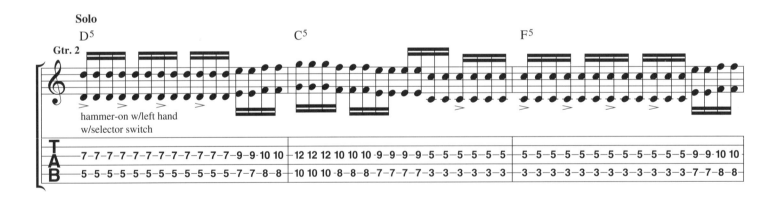

D⁵　　　　　　　　　　　　　　　　　C⁵

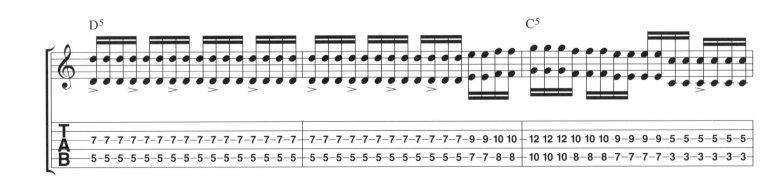

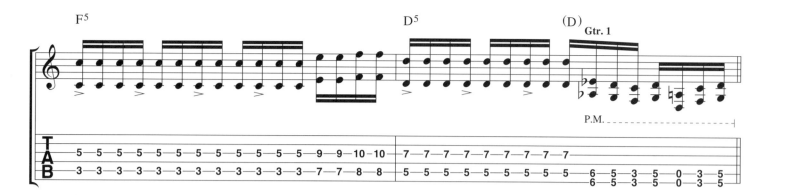

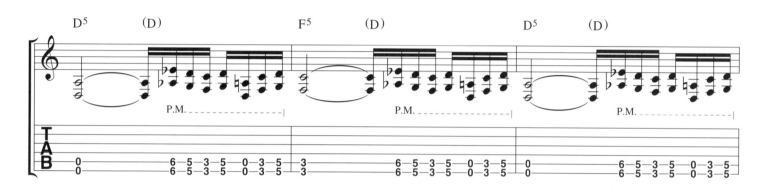

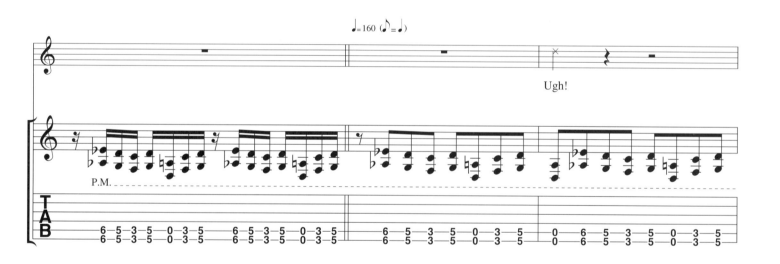

Ugh!

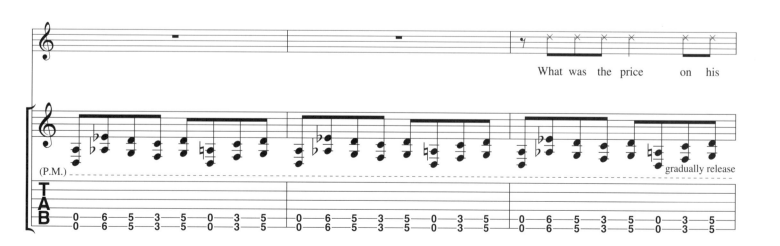

What was the price on his

I think I heard a shot.

I think I

heard   I think I heard a shot.

53

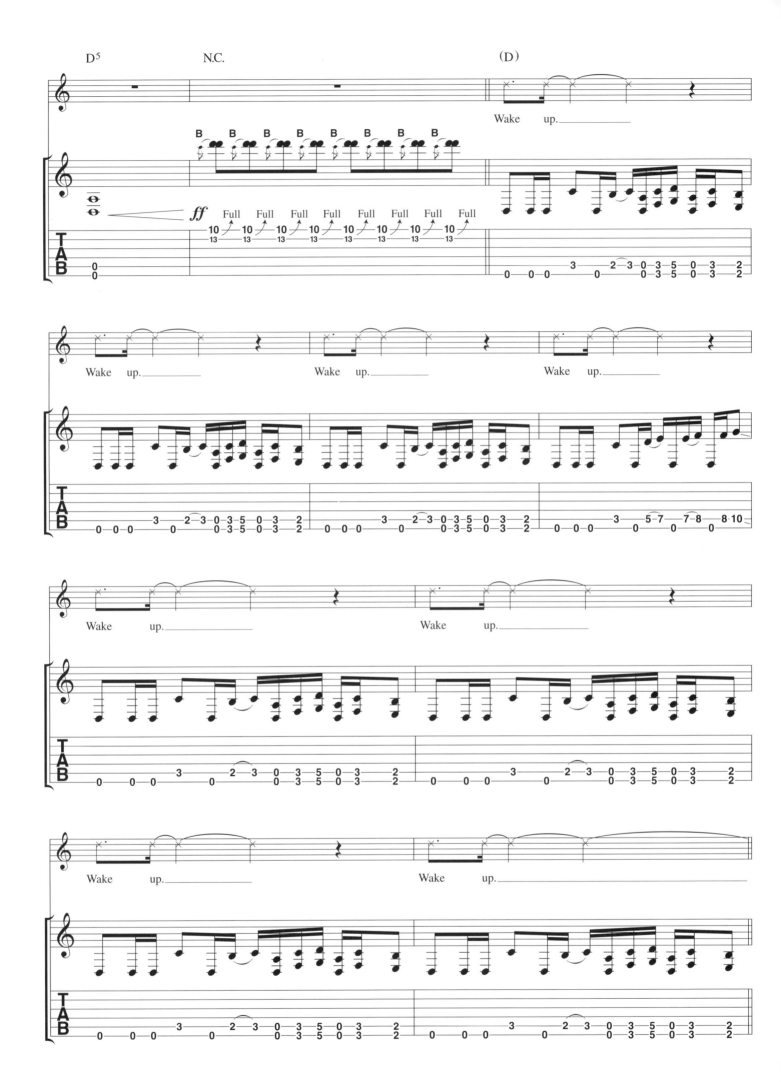

Collect *all* the titles in the series!
play guitar with...

AC/DC
Includes:
back in black
highway to hell
whole lotta rosie
Order No. AM955900

the beatles
Includes:
day tripper
get back
yesterday
Order No. NO90665

the beatles Book 2
Includes:
eight days a week
please please me
ticket to ride
Order No. NO90667

the beatles Book 3
Includes:
here comes the sun
revolution
while my guitar gently weeps
Order No. NO90689

chuck berry
Includes:
around and around
johnny b. goode
no particular place to go
Order No. AM943789

black sabbath
Includes:
iron man
paranoid
war pigs
Order No. AM955911

blur
Includes:
country house
girls and boys
parklife
Order No. AM935320

bon jovi
Includes:
livin' on a prayer
wanted dead or alive
you give love a bad name
Order No. AM92558

eric clapton
Includes:
layla
sunshine of your love
tears in heaven
Order No. AM950862

phil collins
Includes:
another day in paradise
don't lose my number
one more night
Order No. AM928147

the corrs
Includes:
forgiven, not forgotten
so young
what can i do
Order No. AM960971

the cranberries
Includes:
hollywood
ridiculous thoughts
zombie
Order No. AM941699

dire straits
Includes:
money for nothing
romeo and juliet
sultans of swing
Order No. DG70735

free
Includes:
all right now
fire and water
wishing well
Order No. AM960960

david gilmour
Includes:
learning to fly
on the turning away
take it back
Order No.AM954602

buddy holly
Includes:
rave on
words of love
peggy sue
Order No. AM943734

john lee hooker
Includes:
boom boom
the healer
i'm in the mood
Order No. AM951885

b. b. king
Includes:
every day i have the blues
rock me baby
the thrill is gone
Order No. AM951874

the kinks
Includes:
all day and all of the night
waterloo sunset
you really got me
Order No. AM951863

kula shaker
Includes:
govinda
hey dude
hush
Order No. AM943767

john lennon
Includes:
cold turkey
happy xmas (war is over)
woman
Order No. AM943756

bob marley
Includes:
i shot the sheriff
jamming
no woman, no cry
Order No. AM937739

metallica
Includes:
enter sandman
fade to black
the unforgiven
Order No. AM92559

metallica Book 2
Includes:
creeping death
seek and destroy
whiskey in the jar
Order No. AM955977

alanis morissette
Includes:
hand in my pocket
ironic
you oughta know
Order No. AM943723

oasis
Includes:
cigarettes & alcohol
morning glory
supersonic
Order No. AM935330

ocean colour scene
Includes:
the circle
the day we caught the train
the riverboat song
Order No. AM943712

elvis presley
Includes:
all shook up
blue suede shoes
hound dog
Order No. AM937090

pulp
Includes:
common people
disco 2000
sorted for e's & wizz
Order No. AM938124

the rolling stones
Includes:
brown sugar
(i can't get no) satisfaction
jumpin' jack flash
Order No. AM90247

stereophonics
Includes:
just looking
pick a part that's new
the bartender & the thief
Order No. AM960950

sting
Includes:
an englishman in new york
fields of gold
if you love somebody
 set them free
Order No. AM928092

the stone roses
Includes:
i am the resurrection
i wanna be adored
ten storey love song
Order No. AM943701

the stone roses Book 2
Includes:
fool's gold
love spreads
one love
Order No. AM955890

suede
Includes:
animal nitrate
electricity
we are the pigs
Order No. AM955955

paul weller
Includes:
the changingman
out of the sinking
wild wood
Order No. AM937827

the who
Includes:
i can see for miles
pinball wizard
substitute
Order No. AM955867

the 60's
Includes:
all along the watchtower
 (jimi hendrix)
born to be wild (steppenwolf)
not fade away (the rolling stones)
Order No. AM957748

the 70's
Includes:
all right now (free)
hotel california (the eagles)
live and let die (wings)
Order No. AM957759

the 80's
Includes:
addicted to love (robert palmer)
need you tonight (inxs)
where the streets have no
 name (u2)
Order No. AM957760

the 90's
Includes:
everything must go
 (manic street preachers)
love is the law (the seahorses)
wonderwall (oasis)
Order No. AM957770

blues legends
Includes:
crossroads blues (cream)
couldn't stand the weather
 (stevie ray vaughan)
killing floor (jimi hendrix)
Order No. AM958507

classic tracks
Includes:
every breath you take (the police)
hey joe (jimi hendrix)
ziggy stardust (david bowie)
Order No. AM961004

pop anthems
Includes:
angels (robbie williams)
road rage (catatonia)
what can i do (the corrs)
Order No. AM960982

the metal album
Includes:
fade to black (metallica)
live and let die (guns n' roses)
love bites (def leppard)
Order No. AM954426

the gold book
Includes:
johnny b. goode (chuck berry)
layla (eric clapton)
sultans of swing (dire straits)
Order No. AM951907

the platinum book
Includes:
a design for life (manic street
 preachers)
cigarettes & alcohol (oasis)
the riverboat song
 (ocean colour scene)
Order No. AM951918

... and many more!